The

Positive

Power of

Holiness

The Positive Power of Holiness

by Ruth Rieder

An Interactive
Study Guide for
Power Before the Throne
and _Reflecting the Glory_

The Positive Power of Holiness

*Unless otherwise indicated, all Scripture quotations are taken
from the King James Version of the Bible.*

ISBN: 0-9674360-3-6

FOR INFORMATION CONTACT:
Ruth Rieder
P. O. Box 15252
Rio Rancho, NM 87174

Printed in the United States by
Morris Publishing
3212 E. Hwy 30
Kearney, NE 68847
1-800-650-7888

Dedicated to every obedient soul
who desires to grow in the grace
and knowledge of our Lord and
Saviour, Jesus Christ.

Acknowledgments

I wish to express my heartfelt love and gratitude to Donna Ten Eyck and Darie Scott for their time, effort, and valuable input on this study guide. Ladies, I could not have done it without your help!

Special thanks to Bethany Sledge for editing, formatting, and proofing this project.

Above all else, to God be the glory for everything He has done!

Table of Contents

Part One:

Power Before

The Throne

I.
Revelation
Or Perish!

A.   The true foundation for obedience to God is (I John 5:3; Psalm 111:10):

    1.   _____

    2.   _____

B.   To whom does God entrust His secrets (Psalm 25:14)?_____

_____

_____

C.   Obedience to Him will become our number one priority when _____ (Deuteronomy 6:5; Matthew 22:37-38; Mark 12:30).

D.   God commands His people to be _____
        from the world (Leviticus 20:24; II Corinthians
        6:17-18).

E.   Casting off the restraints of separation from the
        world (James 4:4) will cause you to become a:
        1.   _____ of God and
        2.   _____ of the world.

F.   The apostle Paul describes those who walk con-
        trary to God's Word in Philippians 3:17-20 as
        _____: Whose
        1.   _____,
        2.   _____, and
        3.   _____,
        4.   _____.

G.   II Peter 2:20-22 gives a vivid illustration of the
        consequences to those who walk contrary to the
        Word of God.
        1.   List these consequences:
                a.   _____
                b.   _____
                c.   _____

2.   What are they likened to?

    a.   _____

    b.   _____

H.   What other key ingredient will aid us in our obedience to God? _____

I.   According to Proverbs 29:18, what causes people to perish? _____

1.   The word "vision" in the Hebrew language is the word _____, which means _____.

2.   The word "perish" is the Hebrew word _____, meaning: _____;

    _____; _____;

    _____; _____;

    _____; _____;

    _____; _____;

    _____; _____;

    _____.

J.   The NIV translation states: *"Where there is no revelation _____ _____ _____ _____ _____; but blessed is he who keeps the law."*

K.   We must have _____ or we will
      _____!

II.
Role Reversal vs. God's Order

A.   According to I Corinthians 11:3, what is God's order of authority for the Church?

1. _____

2. _____

3. _____

4. _____

B.   The husband is the head of the wife (Ephesians 5:23, 25-28, 31, 33; and I Peter 3:7). He is responsible for her

1. _____,

2. _____, and

3. _____.

C. A woman should respond to her husband with _____ and _____ (Ephesians 5:22, 24, 33; and I Peter 3:1, 5-6).

D. What symbolizes our place in God's order of authority?
    1. For men: _____
    2. For women: _____

E. Give the definition of the following:
    1. Shave _____
    2. Shorn _____
    3. Shear _____
    4. Trim _____

F. There is a difference between cutting and trimming hair. **True** or **False**

G. What is the proper definition for the covering that is in question (I Corinthians 11:15)?
    _____

H. What word in I Corinthians 11:6 causes us to realize it is wrong for a woman to cut her hair?

    _____

I. List five things that are a shame according to Scripture.
    1. _____
    2. _____
    3. _____
    4. _____
    5. _____

J. According to Deuteronomy 21:10-14, what was involved in the humiliation process of the female captives?
    1. _____
    2. _____

K. I Corinthians 11:7 states the woman is the glory of the man. What is the definition of glory?

    _____

    _____

L. Proverbs 12:4 describes a virtuous woman as a _____ to her husband. A _____ is a symbol of:

1. _____,
2. _____, and
3. _____.

M.   What two words did Paul use in I Corinthians 11:6 and 7 to describe the consequences of our actions?

1. _____
2. _____

N.   Uncut hair on men and cut hair on women is an outward _____ of an inward _____ called lack of _____.

O.   What teaches us that it is a shame for a man to have long hair (I Corinthians 11:13-14)?

_____

P.   Deuteronomy 22:5 uses what word to describe God's view of "cross dressing"? _____

Q.   Abominations to _____ may change, but abominations to _____ never change.

R. List ten things that are an abomination to God.

1. _____
2. _____
3. _____
4. _____
5. _____
6. _____
7. _____
8. _____
9. _____
10. _____

S. Working an abomination in the sight of God cannot bar you from the New Jerusalem or blot your name out of the Lamb's book of life. **True** or **False**

T. Role reversal was very apparent in our society during _____ when women began to wear _____ _____ and assumed a _____ _____ in the factories.

U. In Isaiah 14:12-14, who was involved in the greatest role reversal that has ever taken place? _____

21

V.   Our _____ and our _____ are outward signs of our inward condition.

W.   We are either occupying our place in _____

_____, or we are trying to stage a

_____ _____.

III.
The Million Dollar Question

A. Define the two Greek words Paul used concerning hair in I Corinthians 11:14-15.
1. "Komao" _____
2. "Kome" _____

B. In light of these two words, the issue is not _____ or _____ hair but is _____ hair.

C. What two hereditary factors determine a person's hair length?
1. _____
2. _____

D. What must a woman who has cut or trimmed her

hair do in order to regain her proper place in God's order? _____

E.   The Bible plainly states in I Corinthians 11:15 that a woman's _____ *is given her for a*

_____.

1.   The word "for" is the Greek word _____.

2.   This word means _____.

F.   What is the answer to our "Million Dollar Question" of "How long is long hair?"

_____

IV.
Who Really Is
In Bondage?

A.   According to Isaiah 30:1-2, it is possible to have the wrong covering. **True** or **False**

B.   Throughout Scripture Egypt has always typified _____ and the place of _____.

C.   Society is influenced by the media, but according to Psalm 1:1 a person is blessed when

_____.

D.   The Church is described in I Peter 2:9.

    1.   What are the four descriptive phrases used to portray the Church?

        a.   _____

        b.   _____

        c. _____

        d. _____

2. What have we been called to do?

_____

      a. The Greek word for "praises" is _____, meaning _____.

      b. Define virtue. _____

_____

_____

_____

E. God does not want a _____, _____, _____ version of His Church. He wants a _____, _____, and _____ Church.

F. Properly showing forth the _____ of God identifies us as followers of _____ or _____.

G. The Church has been espoused to one _____ that we may be presented to Christ as a _____ _____ (II Corinthians 11:2). God wants a bride who:

1. Has been _____ to him and

2.   Has not defiled herself with the ways of

_____.

H.   Modern women shed their _____ and cover up with _____, which is not the covering of the _____.

I.   We need to get our counsel from the _____ and not from Egypt's _____.

J.   What does Psalm 144:12 liken our children to?
1.   Sons: _____
2.   Daughters: _____

K.   What is another insult that Egypt heaps upon women?_____

_____

L.   God's creation can be improved with a covering of paint. **True** or **False**

M.   We have been born into the Church that is _____ and have been made _____ from the law of _____ and _____ (Galatians 4:26; Romans 8:2; John 8:36).

27

N.　During the Roaring Twenties what major discovery affected fashion trends?

　　_____

　　1.　Name three of these trends:

　　　　a.　_____

　　　　b.　_____

　　　　c.　_____

　　2.　What Egyptian symbols of slavery were adopted?

　　　　a.　_____

　　　　b.　_____

O.　*"So then, brethren, we are not children of the _____, but of the _____. Stand fast therefore in the _____wherewith Christ hath made us _____, and be not _____ again with the yoke of _____ "* (Galatians 4:31; 5:1).

P.　Where can true liberty and freedom be found?

　　_____

Q.　Who really is in bondage? _____

　　_____

V.
We Have No Such Custom!

A. *"But if any man seem to be _____, we have no such _____, neither the churches of God"* (I Corinthians 11:16).

B. According to history, what did women sacrifice during the annual mourning for the death of Aphrodite's lover Adonis? _____

C. What major deity did young Greek maidens worship in the Grecian Empire? _____
   1. Her image was believed to have fallen down from _____ (Acts 19:35).
   2. Where was the temple that housed this statue? _____

D. Who was instrumental in inciting a riot in response to Paul's teachings in Acts 19 and what was his trade?

    1. _____

    2. _____

E. What did the prostitutes in the temple of Diana have in common and why?

    1. _____

    2. _____

F. What three things did young girls offer to Diana before marriage?

    1. _____

    2. _____

    3. _____

G. In light of these customs, explain why Paul wrote I Corinthians 11. _____

_____

_____

_____

_____

_____

H.   What guise does the worship of female deities assume today?

      1.   _____

      2.   _____

      3.   _____

I.   In your own words, explain how Paul's day parallels the modern world. _____

_____

_____

_____

_____

_____

J.   According to Jeremiah 7:29, what does cutting the hair and casting it away symbolize? _____

_____

K.   What caused Israel's separation from God (Jeremiah 7:30-34)?_____

L.   What was the end result of their anarchy against God as described in Jeremiah 7:30-34?

_____

_____

M.   What did the apostle Paul liken our natural bodies to in I Corinthians 6:19-20, and what did he command us to do in our body and spirit?

1. _____

2. _____

N.   As an holy priesthood what kind of sacrifices are we to offer up to God? _____

O.   The heathenish rites of this world can never be incorporated into the _____ that takes place in the _____ that are inhabited by the _____ _____. *"We have no such custom, neither the churches of God!"*

VI.
Guardians Of
The Glory

A. What Scriptural references place the Cherubim beside the throne of God?

    1. _____

    2. _____

    3. _____

B. According to Ezekiel 28:14 where was Lucifer's delegated place of authority? _____

    1. Who placed him there? _____

    2. What did he cover? _____

C. What caused Lucifer's rebellion (Ezekiel 28:17)?_____

_____

D.   Lucifer was full of _____, but his
     _____ was _____ by reason of
     _____ _____.

E.   As the cycle of _____ _____
     continues to spin, even men are caught up in this
     _____ _____ of _____.

F.   Why do we battle with cut or dyed hair, make-
     up, fingernail polish, jewelry, and improper
     clothing?_____

     _____

G.   Focusing on the desire to be beautiful will
     corrupt our _____, causing us to
     _____ the paltry things of _____
     _____ above our relationship with our
     _____.

H.   What will happen when we value our
     appearance above the law of God?_____

     _____

I.   In I Timothy 2:12 God commands a woman not
     to usurp authority over whom? _____

1.   What relationship does this refer to?
_____

2.   What power does a woman have over her husband? _____

J.   What spirit can be strong enough to persuade someone to part with the promise of eternal life and why?

1.   _____

2.   _____

K.   What is the warning given to the Church in I John 2:15-17? _____

_____

1.   Name the three things of the world that are not of the Father.

a.   _____

b.   _____

c.   _____

L.   We are _____ of Christ, _____ known and _____ of all _____.

M.   God is a God of _____ and _____.

N. *"Out of Zion, the_____ of_____,*
    God hath _____ " (Psalm 50:2).

O. What is the significance of the covering in
    Ezekiel 28:14 and 16? _____

    _____

    1. What was Lucifer's main responsibility?

        _____

    2. What did he lose once he was cast out?

        _____

    3. Who did God delegate Lucifer's lost
        estate to? _____

P. According to I Corinthians 11:10 and 15, what
    is the Glory connected with?_____
    1. What is a woman's covering? _____
    2. Where does her power reside? _____

Q. Why does the enemy tempt women to tamper
    with their covering?_____

    _____

R. Women are now the _____ of the
    _____, not her _____ but the _____
    of _____.

S.   What does a woman's hair signal to the spirit world?

1. _____

2. _____

T.   There are two types of angels. What are they?

1. _____

2. _____

U.   When a woman _____ her head, she removes the _____. This parallels with Lucifer how?

1. _____

2. _____

3. _____

V.   Where is another place you find the covering, the angels, and the glory?_____

W.   To forfeit the _____ was to forfeit the _____ _____.

X.   The token of our _____ _____ _____ is the _____ _____ through _____ in _____ _____.

Y.   Without the covering of the blood, what are we exposed to? _____

Z.   The woman as God created her is a picture of the Church.
   1.   What are the six things describing her as such?
      a.   _____
      b.   _____
      c.   _____
      d.   _____
      e.   _____
      f.   _____
   2.   What makes her visible and recognizable as the bride of Christ?_____

AA. When the glory of the Lord departed from the house or the Temple, what did the Cherubim do (Ezekiel 10:18-19)?_____
   _____
   1.   What were the Cherubim committed to?
      _____

BB. We are the temples of the _____ _____, and the _____ is in residence as long as our

_____ and _____ in the creation order are maintained through _____ and _____ _____.

CC. What is severed from a woman's life when she cuts her hair? _____

   1. Where there is no glory, the angels are absent except for _____.

DD. Name the six areas of protection encompassed in the armor of God (Ephesians 6:10-18).

   1. _____
   2. _____
   3. _____
   4. _____
   5. _____
   6. _____

EE. According to Isaiah 58:8, what provides protection for our backs or is our rearguard? _____

   _____

FF. Titus 2:5 states that women are to be _____ _____ _____.

   1. The Greek definition offers a deeper

meaning other than simply housekeeping. What is it? _____

2.   What does rebellion invite into our homes?_____

GG. A woman's uncut hair provides protection for whom?_____

HH. List four things a virtuous woman provides to her husband (Proverbs 31:11-12).

1. _____
2. _____
3. _____
4. _____

II.   What an _____ _____, yet what a _____ _____ that God has _____ to the woman.

JJ.   The four questions a woman must ask herself before putting a scissors to her hair are what?

1. _____
2. _____
3. _____
4. _____

KK. What in Lucifer's covering contributed to his vanity? _____

LL. According to I Timothy 2:9 and I Peter 3:3, what two things are we not to adorn ourselves with?
1. _____
2. _____

MM. In light of the culture of Paul's day, why did he focus on the wearing of pearls?
1. _____
2. _____
3. _____

NN. What do we have that is far more valuable than gold or precious stones?
1. _____
2. _____

OO. Our salvation is not worth more than a few inferior Egyptian baubles. **True** or **False**
1. Our _____ reveal what we _____ most.

PP.   If we are in obedience to God's Word, what
       promise do we have? _____

       _____

QQ.   What is the role of the husband to his wife in
       God's creation order? _____
       1.   Why did God place the husband in this
             role? _____
       2.   What is the key to effectively guarding
             the glory and insuring divine protection
             for your family? _____

RR.   How does Ezekiel describe the Cherubim in
       Ezekiel 10:12, and what are they watchers of?
       1.   _____
       2.   _____

SS.   *"The _____ of the LORD _____*
       round about them that _____ him, and
       _____ them" (Psalm 34:7).

TT.   What role do angels fulfil, and to whom do they
       minister (Hebrews 1:14)?
       1.   _____
       2.   _____

UU. What do we sacrifice for the sake of vanity and temporary indulgence in Egypt's fleshpots?

_____

VV. What four things does Proverbs 4:26-27 admonish us to do?

1. _____
2. _____
3. _____
4. _____

WW. What must we constantly guard against as saints of the Most High God? _____

XX. We must examine our _____ and remove our _____ from evil because the _____ of _____ discerns our _____ by how we _____ it.

YY. We are reminded of a highway in the discourse that Isaiah 35. What does the highway concern?

_____

1. What is it called? _____
2. Who will not be able to enter in? _____

_____

ZZ.   The highway that leads to _____ _____
       _____ and the resulting harvest is not the
       _____, _____ way of _____,
       but it is the _____ and _____ way
       called "_____."

AAA.   What does Isaiah 62:10 instruct us to do?
       1. _____
       2. _____
       3. _____
       4. _____
       5. _____

BBB.   God is coming back for what type of church?

       _____

CCC.   How can we be kept from the spirit of vanity
       and strong delusion?
       1. _____
       2. _____

DDD.   What does Paul warn us of in II Thessalonians
       2:11-12? _____

       _____

EEE.   May we walk _____ unto all pleasing before the One who has _____ us from the _____ of _____ and has translated us in the _____ of His dear _____!

FFF.   *"Search ____, O God, and _____ my*
_____: try ____, and _____ my
_____: and see if there be any _____
way in ____, and lead me in the _____
_____" (Psalm 139:23-24).

GGG.   To whom did Naboth refuse to give his inheritance to and why?

1.   _____

2.   _____

HHH.   If you let him, the enemy will buy you with:

1.   _____

2.   _____

III.   What does the enemy want to give you in the place of your God-given beauty? _____
_____

JJJ.   According to Ezekiel 28:16 and 18, what is Lucifer? _____

KKK.   Lucifer's promises can cause us to become _____ to our _____.

LLL.   Matthew 4:10 tells us to worship and serve whom? _____

MMM. The spirit that destroyed Lucifer will cause us to sell our inheritance for what?
1. _____
2. _____
3. _____

NNN.   Our _____ will dictate our _____.

OOO.   What is the difference between growing and swelling? _____
_____

PPP.   In order to keep the infection of compromise from invading our lives and churches, we must be _____ of the _____ !

VII.

Power Before The Throne

A.   As the final drama between good and evil unfolds, what does the Church need?

1. _____

2. _____

_____

B.   What paradox will never change? _____

_____

_____

C.   What must we never abdicate? _____

_____

D. *"For this _____ ought the _____ to have _____ on her _____ because of the _____ "* (I Corinthians 11:10).

1. The Greek word for "power" is _____, meaning:

    a. _____,
    b. _____,
    c. _____,
    d. _____,
    e. _____,
    f. _____,
    g. _____ or
    h. _____,
    i. _____.

2. What kind of freedom does this delegated power allow woman to have? _____

    _____

3. Obedient women are not in slavery but are free from what? _____

    _____

    _____

4. What do we need to have as we wage war against the forces of darkness? _____

    _____

E.   In Genesis 3:15, God decreed that there would
be _____ between the _____ and the
_____.

    1.   What is the key to obedience as found in
Genesis 3:16? _____

    2.   What comes as a result of a woman's
submission to her husband, and what is
loosed on her behalf?

        a.   _____

        b.   _____

F.   How does the Church exhibit her submission to
her husband, the Lord Jesus Christ, and what is
the guaranteed result?

    1.   _____

    2.   _____

G.   Our society's moral foundation has been
destroyed as mentioned in Psalm 11:3.

    1.   What are two causes of this erosion?

        a.   _____

        b.   _____

    2.   How must the Church respond to our
society's condition? _____

_____

H.   What does the devil realize that the Church has at its disposal, and why does he desire to take it from us?

1. _____

2. _____

I.   What will happen if we lay our heads in the "lap of wickedness"? _____

_____

J.   In your own words, explain the exhortation of Paul in Romans 16:17-20. _____

_____

_____

_____

_____

K.   A Church that refuses to ____ will be _____ to finalize the _____ of _____.

L.   What is the triumphant promise set forth in Isaiah 60:1-3? _____

_____

_____

M. What kind of day do we live in, what lies fallen in the streets, and what abounds more and more?

    1. _____

    2. _____

    3. _____

N. Who will receive end time revival and the resulting harvest? _____

_____

O. Who has come to the Kingdom for such a time as this and has Power Before The Throne?

_____

NOTES

NOTES

NOTES

NOTES

NOTES

Part Two:

Reflecting

The Glory

I.

God's Gold

A. When God created valuable metals such as silver and gold, where did He place them?

_____

B. How are earthly treasures obtained?
1. _____
2. _____

C. Where can the precious truths of God's Word be found (Colossians 2:3)? _____
1. To whom are they imparted (Jeremiah 29:13)? _____

_____
2. How do you find God? _____

_____

D. An intense pursuit of God is the earmark of what kind of person (Proverbs 18:15)? _____

_____

E. Who wrote about man's intense pursuit of wealth in the depths of the earth? _____

F. Name four things that have not seen or set foot inside the earth's farthest recesses.

   1. _____
   2. _____
   3. _____
   4. _____

G. *"But where can _____ be found? Where does _____ dwell?"*

H. In your own words, describe the incredible value of wisdom (Job 28:13-19). _____

_____

_____

_____

I. What is wisdom concealed from, and who has only heard a rumor of it (Job 28:21-22)?

1. _____
2. _____
3. _____

J. Who knows the way to this treasure trove (Job 28:23)? _____

K. When God looked at wisdom, what three things did He do (Job 28:27)?
   1. _____
   2. _____
   3. _____

L. Give God's definition of wisdom and understanding (Job 28:28). _____
   _____

M. Since God knows the end from the beginning, the holiness questions that confront the modern day church are a surprise to Him. **True** or **False**
   1. Where can the answers be found? _____
   2. How can they be obtained?
      a. _____
      b. _____
      c. _____

N.   According to Proverbs 2:3-6, how should we search for knowledge and understanding, and what will be the end result?

1. _____

2. _____

O.   God's gold supply remains _____, His _____ is _____, and His *"commandment is_____ _____."*

P.   For personal enrichment, memorize Romans 11:33-36.

Gold is found anywhere you stick your shovel, so let's dig deeply and go after **GOD'S GOLD!!**

II.
"Son of the Morning"

A. How does God refer to Himself in Isaiah 44:6?

_____

B. What are two things God states about Himself in Isaiah 46:9?

1. _____
2. _____

C. What are two things God states about what He has declared from ancient times as recorded in Isaiah 46:10?

1. _____
2. _____

D.   What is behind the scenes of our physical existence?_____

E.   How does the apostle Paul describe the things that are seen as written in II Corinthians 4:18?

_____

    1.   How are the unseen things described?

    _____

    2.   What do the visible things reflect?

    _____

F.   When God set His divine plan in motion, what did He fashion?_____

G.   Who was present and shouted for joy when God created the heavens and earth (Job 38:7)?

_____

H.   The Word of God identifies three angels by name. List their names and the meaning of each name.
    1.   _____
    2.   _____
    3.   _____

I.	Where does Gabriel's name first appear in the Bible, and what was his first assignment as God's messenger?

　　1. _____

　　2. _____

J.	In the first chapter of Luke, Gabriel appeared to two people. Who were they, and what message did he bring to each of them?

　　1. _____
　　_____

　　2. _____
　　_____

K.	How long did Daniel fast and pray for understanding (Daniel 10:1-3)? _____

L.	When did the first angel attempt to bring spiritual enlightenment to Daniel, and who resisted him (Daniel 10:10-13)?

　　1. _____
　　2. _____

M.	Name the angel sent to intervene on Daniel's behalf. _____

N.   The angel informed Daniel that the conflict would only intensify when he returned to fight with Michael. Who would join forces with the Prince of Persia to fight against them (Daniel 10:20-21)? _____

O.   In Jude, Michael contended with the devil concerning whose body (Jude 9)? _____

P.   In the war that took place in Revelation 12:7-12, who was involved, and who prevailed?
      1.   _____
      2.   _____

Q.   Throughout Scripture, how is Michael portrayed? _____

R.   In what attribute did Lucifer differ from all other angelic creatures? _____

S.   Lucifer was created *"full of* _____*, and* _____ *in* _____ *"* (Ezekiel 28:12).

T.   Describe Lucifer's appearance. _____
      _____

U.   From what point of reference do we seek to understand the spirit realm? _____

_____

V.   How is God often pictured, and what is His true essence?

1.   _____

     _____

2.   _____

W.   What was God's response to Moses' desire to see His glory (Exodus 33:20)? _____

_____

_____

X.   What did Jesus tell His disciples in Luke 24:39?

_____

_____

1.   What was His message to the Jews in John 5:37? _____

     _____

2.   *"No man hath _____ God at _____ _____." "No man hath _____ [Him], nor can _____ [Him]"* (John 1:18; I Timothy 6:16).

Y.   In your own words, what did Solomon say about God in his prayer of dedication (II Chronicles 6:18)? _____

_____

Z.   According to Acts 17:28, of whom are we the offspring?

   1.   _____

   2.   What three things are we dependent on Him for?

      a.   _____

      b.   _____

      c.   _____

AA.   What is the distinct fashion in which God manifests His glory (Psalm 104:1-2; I John 1:5; I Timothy 6:16; Acts 9:3; Revelation 21:23)? _____

BB.   God is _____, and He _____ His _____ in the form of _____.

CC.   From the beginning, Lucifer was created with what ability to praise God? _____

1.　　Where did he minister before the Lord?

_____

2.　　What would the strains of skillful music involve? _____

DD.　When the _____ of God's _____ descended, it came in contact with Lucifer's _____ _____, resulting in a _____ of _____ _____.

EE.　What was Lucifer called in Ezekiel 28:14 and 16?

1.　_____

2.　_____

FF.　What is the Hebrew word for "covereth" and "covering"?

1.　_____

2.　The meaning of this word is what?

a.　_____

b.　_____

c.　_____

d.　_____

e.　_____

GG. What was the grave responsibility linked to the position of high honor which Lucifer held?

_____

HH. What was Lucifer's source of splendor rooted in, and without this what would happen to his brilliance?

1. _____

2. _____

II. As Lucifer allowed the deception of pride to enter, what did he say in his heart (Isaiah 14:13-14)?

1. _____

_____

_____

_____

2. Who was persuaded to take part in his rebellion? _____

JJ. What did Lucifer's proud ambitions fill him with (Ezekiel 28:16)? _____

KK. What did Jesus say Lucifer was from the beginning (John 8:44)? _____

LL. What three things did pride over outward appearance birth?

1. _____

2. _____

3. _____

MM. What two things were at the root of Lucifer's anarchy against God, and what was corrupted (Ezekiel 28:17)?

1. _____

2. _____

3. _____

NN. What was the end result of Lucifer's pride (Luke 10:18)? _____

OO. What vacancy did the expulsion of Lucifer leave in the heavenly realm? _____
_____

PP. Who did God create to fill this role (Genesis 1:27)? _____

QQ. Unable to _____ God, Lucifer continually seeks to _____ God's image and to

_____ it with _____ _____.

RR.　What are the perfect weapons satan uses in the destruction of mankind?

　　1.　_____

　　2.　_____

SS.　What is encompassed in true holiness?

　　1.　_____

　　2.　_____

TT.　What does the prince of darkness desire to destroy? _____

UU.　In Matthew 5:14, Jesus portrays the purpose of God's people as what? _____

VV.　Who is the source of spiritual illumination in a dark world? _____

WW.　What is our mission?_____

XX.　What do our good works, namely a godly, separated lifestyle, result in? _____

_____

YY. The wondrous privilege of worshiping the Creator and reflecting His glory was taken from whom and bestowed upon whom?

1. _____

2. _____

ZZ. Let your _____ shine, never _____ it under a _____, and "don't let _____ blow it _____!!"

III.
It All Starts at the Top

A. In what direction did the anointing oil flow according to Psalm 133:2? _____

B. God's glory begins at the _____ and flows _____.

C. When God created mankind, He ordained what (Genesis 1:27)?_____

D. Man was to be the _____ of God's image while the woman would be the _____ of the Church, God's _____.

E. Why must not a man cover his head, and who is the glory of the man (I Corinthians 11:7)?

1. _____

2. _____

F. What are the masculine characteristics of a man a representation of? _____
   1. The feminine attributes of a woman are a glory to whom representing whom?
      a. _____
      b. _____
   2. How does the Church glorify God?
      _____

G. What question did Paul address when dealing with the subject of God's order in I Corinthians 11? _____

H. What has been a major source of identity for men and women?
   1. Men: _____
   2. Women: _____

I. In satan's attempt to destroy God's image, what has been attacked? _____
   _____

J.   In the destruction of this vital area, what is distorted? _____

K.   The onset of "unisex" clothing and hairstyles is not innocent. **True** or **False**

L.   What hidden agenda is behind it all? _____
       _____

M.   Our hair is indicative of our relationship with God in what way? _____
       _____

N.   Lucifer was once the "_____" cherub and realizes the significance of the _____ and _____ heads.

O.   What must the Church seek to protect in light of this? _____
       _____

P.   The _____ the night, the _____ the light of God's glory will shine forth as we reveal _____ likeness in the _____.

Q. What did David declare in Psalm 139:13? ____

_____

1. How is God involved in the development of human life? _____

2. What did the psalmist ask for after he acknowledged that God had made him and fashioned him? _____

_____

R. God randomly chose our unique characteristics and the color of our hair, skin, and eyes. **True** or **False**

S. What can we do to alter our stature (Matthew 6:27)? _____

T. Is it humanly possible to change the color of our hair permanently (Matthew 5:36)? **Yes** or **No**

U. What happens to God's design and image when you dye your hair?

1. _____

2. _____

V. Two questions we must ask concerning hair dye
are:
1. _____
2. _____

W. How does God view white or silver hair
(Proverbs 16:31)? _____

X. Man's short hair and woman's long hair are
reflections of _____ _____; however, as
hair whitens with age, it becomes a _____
_____, the crown being a _____
_____.

Y. According to Proverbs 20:29, where is the glory
of the young and the beauty of the old?
1. _____
2. _____

Z. As we age, who do we become a greater reflec-
tion of? _____
1. How was hair described in Daniel 7:9 and
again in Revelation 1:13-15?
a. _____
b. _____

2. What was the color symbolic of?

_____

AA. As your hair whitens, what does it symbolize and what does it cause you to become?

1. _____
2. _____

BB. List two things you should never touch.

1. _____
2. _____

CC. If the _____ of _____ is not handled _____, serious _____ are the _____.

DD. What happened when Lucifer ceased to protect the glory of God? _____

EE. May the _____ _____ flow from our _____ down to the _____ of our _____.

FF. Where does it all start? _____

IV.
Don't Veil
the Glory

A. Where do we find the recorded use of makeup in Western cultures? _____

   1. What city was renowned for its painted women? _____

   2. What are two other things that character-ized this city?

      a. _____
      b. _____

B. Why did the prostitutes use exotic eye makeup?

   _____

C. Makeup was also used in idol worship. Why?

   1. _____
   2. _____

D.   Throughout the centuries, what four things did cosmetics remain synonymous with?

1. _____
2. _____
3. _____
4. _____

E.   Name one of the religious groups that staunchly forbade the use of paint. _____

F.   How did Thomas Tuke depict the painted face in his 1616 *Discourse Against Painting and Tincturing?* _____

G.   Poet John Dunne stated that women who _____ _____ the _____ order, taking "the _____ out of _____ hand."

H.   What did some people view the cosmetic arts as a form of? _____

I.   For the majority of the nineteenth century, face painting was acceptable among respectable people. **True** or **False**

J.   For most Americans during the 1800s, what did a painted woman typify? _____

_____

K.   What two things were so closely associated in newspapers, tracts, and songs as to be a generic figure of speech?

    1.   _____

    2.   _____

L.   What caused the first hairline cracks in the wall of resistance? _____

M.   Name two people who appeared in cosmetic advertisements and testimonials during the 1880s, and identify their profession.

    1.   _____

    2.   _____

    3.   _____

N.   Makeup _____ began to _____ from the _____ into _____ _____, heightening the _____ of _____ _____ and _____.

O.   When standardized models of beauty were introduced, what techniques were used that challenged the "natural" look? _____

_____

P.   Painted women remained spectacles to a significant extent prior to what world event? _____

Q.   What would happen to women who appeared on the job with an "artificial complexion"? _____

_____

R.   What did public authorities try in vain to preserve? _____

S.   In 1915, what kind of law did a Kansas legislator propose?_____

_____

_____

T.   Several years later, policewomen in Newark collared teenage girls at the train stations. What happened?_____

_____

_____

U.   In each of the aforementioned circumstances, what did paint imply? _____

_____

V.   Who in particular maintained these conventional views and remained opposed to the use of makeup? _____

    1.   _____ continued to see _____ as a _____ of _____ and _____.

    2.   How did most men view "every painted or flashily dressed woman"? _____

    _____

W.   Who was a prominent makeup artist for movie stars who began to package and sell his products out of his makeup studio? _____

X.   Name two women who opened beauty salons on Fifth Avenue in New York City, and tell what kind of products they initially promoted.

    1.   _____

    2.   _____

    3.   _____

    _____

Y.   After World War I, what did women's growing acceptance of beautifying products blossom into? _____

Z.   From _____ skin _____ to dime store _____, new goods made their _____ into the _____ as _____ soared.

AA.   Who participated in this new form of revenue? _____

    1.   What caused their former convictions about this questionable practice to be discarded? _____

    2.   When did regular beauty columns become standard fare in most women's magazines? _____

BB.   With the inception of mass marketing, what ensued and what were women being conditioned to believe?

    1.   _____

    2.   _____

CC.   Cosmetic ads continually remind women of what? _____

DD. The painted face had suddenly become _____
_____ _____ _____ _____. What had
once been _____ as _____was now
_____ as _____!

EE. How did cosmetics evolve into the giant
industry it is today? _____

    1. When were makeup features in magazines
rare? _____

    2. Where do movie stars appear today, and
what do they promote?

        a. _____

        b. _____

    3. What can the "girl next door" become
with the help of makeup products? _____
_____

FF. Name three things that used to be seen as
women's vices, and tell what they are now a
sign of.

    1. _____

    2. _____

    3. _____

    4. _____

GG. Beauty manuals and women's magazines urged women to encourage narcissism in their daughters. Define narcissism. _____

_____

HH. Asserting women's "right to ROMANCE," advertisements offered cosmetics as what?

    1.   _____

    2.   _____

    3.   Advertisers claimed these items were to be used in the proper quest for what?

        a.   _____

        b.   _____

    4.   According to one beauty guide, what were men like and why should women use cosmetics?

        a.   _____

        b.   _____

II. During the 1920s and 1930s, how did the cosmetic producers, beauty experts, and advertisers shift the burden of female identity? _____

_____

    1.   What was their claim concerning make-up?_____

2.   What was making over a means of? _____

_____

JJ.   Identify the true motive underlying all the skill-ful advertising techniques and high sounding ideals. _____

KK.   What were women brainwashed into believing?

_____

LL.   The use of makeup started as a cry for liberation and a bid for freedom from restraints. State what it has really become and describe the outcome of this assault on women.

1.   _____

2.   _____

_____

_____

MM.   Why was makeup originally used? _____

_____

1.   What are ambitious entrepreneurs and beauty experts striving to prove and pro-claim today? _____

_____

2. In fact, what is the primary purpose of female makeup? _____

3. Makeup is really innocent. **True** or **False**

NN. How was Lucifer created, and what was he the epitome of as he reflected God's glory?

1. _____

2. _____

OO. Describe how his separation from God affected his outward appearance (Isaiah 14:16-17). _____

_____

PP. How does Lucifer enhance his appearance now?

_____

QQ. What was Lucifer's first order of business, and what initial guise did he assume in order to carry out his plan?

1. _____

2. _____

RR. Who was beguiled through satan's subtlety? ___

SS. What happened to God's image when she

partook of the forbidden fruit? _____

TT. State whether or not satan's strategy has changed, and tell what he continually says to mankind.

1. _____

2. _____

_____

UU. Name four masquerades assumed by Lucifer (Revelation 11:7, 12:3-9, 13:11-15, 20:10; I John 4:3; II Thessalonians 2:3-4).

1. _____

2. _____

3. _____

4. _____

VV. Why does the apostle Peter tell us to be sober and vigilant in I Peter 5:8? _____

_____

1. Who is the true Lion, the Lion of the tribe of Judah? _____

2. How is an unsuspecting soul devoured by the devil? _____

WW.   According to II Corinthians 11:14, what does satan transform himself into, and what, in reality, is his light (Matthew 6:23)?

1. _____

2. _____

XX.   Who is the greatest makeup artist that ever existed? _____

YY.   Consider for a moment the words "makeup" and "made-up." What do they depict? _____

_____

ZZ.   Why do we not make up (I John 2:21)? _____

_____

AAA.   Who are we created in the image of (Genesis 1:27)? _____

BBB.   If we are _____ in _____ _____, why would we want to alter His _____?

CCC.   What lie does satan tell us? _____

_____

DDD. Identify two things that makeup has always been synonymous with throughout Scripture.

   1. _____

   2. _____

EEE. Name an extremely wicked woman whose influence contaminated two nations. _____

   1. What nations did she contaminate?

      a. _____

      b. _____

   2. How did she seek to eliminate the worship of God? _____

   3. What practice was included in her idolatrous lifestyle (II Kings 9:30)? _____

   _____

FFF. As Israel and Judah chose to follow the ways of the heathen, what did they begin to do?

   1. _____

   2. _____

GGG. How did Jeremiah and Ezekiel portray these backslidden nations (Jeremiah 4:30; Ezekiel 23:40)? _____

HHH. The human face is created in whose image, and what purpose does it serve?

    1. _____

    2. _____

III. Who illustrates this principle beautifully?____

    1. How long did he commune with God on the top of Mt. Sinai? _____

    2. What emanated from his face? _____

    3. What was it a testimony of? _____

JJJ. How did Aaron and children of Israel respond and why? _____

_____

    1. What were they reminded of? _____

    2. In response to their request, what did Moses wear? _____

KKK. In II Corinthians 3, the apostle Paul writes about this incident in the Old Testament. In your own words, explain what Paul is saying in verses 7 through 9. _____

_____

_____

_____

LLL. As Paul draws the parallel between the two
covenants, what does he focus on? _____

_____

MMM. Describe the difference in the glory of the Old
Testament and that of the New Testament.
1.   Old Testament: _____
2.   New Testament: _____

NNN. From what have we been liberated, and where
does that liberty shine forth?
1.   _____
2.   _____

OOO. *"But we all, with _____ _____ beholding
as in a _____ the _____ of the _____,
are _____ into that same _____ from
_____ to _____, even as by the _____
of the _____"* (II Corinthians 3:18).

PPP. The glory of God can only reflect in what kind
of face? _____
1.   Do we need cosmetics to enhance our
appearance? _____

2. What is the only beautifying agent that a saint of God needs? _____

3. What does He beautify us with (Psalm 149:4)? _____

QQQ. Max Factor, Maybelline, and Revlon cannot compete with God's beauty technique. **True** or **False**

RRR. Do not fall prey to the enemy's lies. Don't ever _____ the _____!

V.
All That Glitters Is Not Good

A. Name two things that precious stones do.

    1. _____

    2. _____

B. Who do they call attention to, and what do they foster?

    1. _____

    2. _____

C. Where did these sparkling jewels originate, and why were they created (Ezekiel 28:13)?

    1. _____

    2. _____

D. What was the express purpose of precious stones? _____

E. When Lucifer was cast as profane from the mountain of God, what happened to these jewels? _____

F. Since his expulsion from heaven, how does satan use jewelry? _____

G. What does jewelry nourish? _____

H. Why is it essential to remove all traces of the enemy's influence from our lives? _____
_____

I. When satan's influence is removed from our lives, what will happen? _____
_____

J. Precious stones will be used again to reflect God's glory. **True** or **False**

K. What is God using jewels for? _____
_____

L.   Who will reflect God's splendor forever and ever (Malachi 3:17)? _____

M.   The glitter described in Malachi 3:17 is good. **True** or **False**

VI.
Temples of Glory

A. How long has it taken to demolish the walls of conservatism in clothing? _____

B. Describe the clothing worn by men and women throughout the eighteenth and nineteenth centuries. _____
    1. During this time period, what was the length of women's skirts? _____
        _____
    2. A woman who showed her ankles was seen as what kind of woman? _____

C. Men and women's clothing showed marked distinction in their characteristics. What were these differences? _____
    _____

D.   Who launched the first assault on the conventional dress code, and when did this take place?

1.   _____

2.   _____

      a.   What kind of garments did they dare to wear? _____

_____

      b.   What were they dubbed? _____

      c.   Who were they named after? ____

_____

E.   How did America react to such a radical departure from traditional values? _____

_____

1.   Did these untraditional clothes become acceptable at this time? _____

2.   What kind of breakdown resulted from this first attempt to undermine conventional attire? _____

F.   In 1890, who created the likeness of a beautiful woman that epitomized the Victorian ideal, and what was his occupation?

1.   _____

2.   _____

     a.   What was this all-American icon called? _____

     b.   How long did this icon retain popularity? _____

G.   During the same decade, another attempt was made to introduce more masculine clothing for women. What was this fashion called, and for whom was it designed?

     1.   _____

     2.   _____

H.   How did America react to this second assault on traditional apparel? _____

_____

I.   Describe the fashions that existed at the onset of the twentieth century. _____

_____

J.   How long did these fashions remain unchanged?

_____

K.   What attitudes caused the radical departure from previous fashion norms? _____

L.   Identify the four major factors that contributed to this radical deviation from previous feminine attire and behavior.

1.   _____

_____

   a.   What did women begin to emulate? _____

   b.   Who was the original sex goddess?

_____

   c.   What was she famous for? _____

_____

   d.   What kind of people heavily influenced behavior and fashions?_____

_____

   e.   Does this trend still persist today?

_____

2.   _____

   a.   How were women liberated in the political arena? _____

   b.   What else did they cast aside? ___

_____

   c.   What kind of behavior did the "flapper" openly engage in? _____

_____

_____

3. _____

    a. Describe the fashions that resulted from this discovery. _____

    _____

    _____

    _____

    b. Did these new fashions symbolize freedom or bondage? _____

4. _____

    a. Describe the wartime fashions. ___

    _____

    _____

    _____

    b. After peace broke out, what transpired on the fashion scene? _____

    _____

M. Name three ways women broke away completely from all former fashion traditions.

    1. _____

    2. _____

    3. _____

N. Along with these revolutionary changes, what else became accepted, and how long did it take for this fashion trend finally to become accepted?

1. _____

2. _____

O. Identify the style introduced during the 1930s that would have a great bearing on future fashions. _____

    1. Who made this style popular? _____

    2. Why did she wear this particular mode? _____

P. Clothing later returned to former levels of modesty. **True** or **False**

Q. What fashion trends were followed during the '40s and '50s?

    1. _____

    2. _____

    3. _____

R. During World War II, _____ became totally _____ as a _____ of _____ _____ while women _____ further

in their _____ for _____ and
_____ with men.

S.   How would seeds sown many years earlier affect subsequent decades? _____
_____

T.   When did the fashions of the '20s come full circle again? _____

U.   What did the desensitizing process allow for?
_____

V.   How were the '20s flapper and the '60s ideal similar? _____

    1.   What new fashion was introduced in the '20s? _____

    2.   Who was the model that embodied the '60s ideal? _____

    3.   Where did she take clothing? _____
_____

    4.   What fashion did she introduce? _____
_____

W.   Describe how the sexual revolution that was

begun forty years earlier bore bitter fruit. _____

_____

_____

_____

X.   What was the end result of the '60s revolution?

_____

Y.   Name three styles generated by Rudi Gernreich,
     and explain why he continued to design this type
     of clothing.

   1. _____

   2. _____

   3. _____

   4. _____

   _____

Z.   How did the "cut-up" skirt of the 1930s resur-
     face? _____

AA. What other popular new fashions swept the
     marketplace? _____

   1.   Where did modesty go as the country
        perpetuated its downward spiral? _____

   _____

2. As inhibitions were consistently lowered, how did people respond? _____

_____

BB. THE _____ _____ OF A _____
WAS _____ IN THE _____ WORN
BY ITS _____ !!

CC. Write the fashion quote from James Laver.

_____

_____

DD. How will the moral condition of the Church be manifested? _____

_____

EE. Of what is clothing an outward indication?

_____

FF. "Clothing is _____. They are nothing _____ than the _____ of the _____
made _____."

GG. For thousands of years, how have human beings communicated with each other? _____

HH. Identify three things that you announce through your clothing.

1. _____
2. _____
3. _____

II. What information or misinformation does your attire convey? _____

_____

JJ. How is this information registered? _____

KK. Who understood the communication of clothing from the beginning? _____

LL. What story illustrates this concept perfectly?

_____

MM. How does the Scripture describe the first man and woman when God brought them together (Genesis 2:25)? _____

1. In their state of innocence, what was nonexistent? _____

2. What happened when Adam and Eve ate of the forbidden fruit? _____

3.   What was shattered? _____

NN. What was the first repercussion of the fall of man? _____

    1.   In the wake of disobedience, what kind of clothing did Adam and Eve construct?

        _____

    2.   Were these sufficient to cover them? ____

OO. Describe the clothing God made for Adam and Eve. _____

PP.   The Hebrew word for "coats" is _____, meaning _____.

QQ. Why did God make coats that covered the nakedness of Adam and Eve? _____

        _____

RR.   What gained admittance into the world through sin? _____

    1.   How did this affect humanity? _____

        _____

    2.   What does the destruction of innocence necessitate? _____

SS.   God is not concerned about the kinds of clothing people wear. **True** or **False**

    1.   What did God provide for the first man and woman? _____

    2.   What is God's criterion for clothing?

    _____

TT.   Can modesty be defined by current societal standards? _____

UU.   What is demonstrated in the preceding historical commentary? _____

    _____

VV.   What must God's Church be governed by?

    _____

WW.   How does the psalmist depict God's Word and His righteousness in Psalm 119:89 and 142?

    1.   _____

    2.   _____

XX.   Desensitization by the current culture has affected the Church in what way? _____

    _____

1. What has become commonplace in the House of God? _____

_____

2. Describe the type of clothing being worn freely by the young and old. _____

_____

3. Identify the spirit that is invading the Church. _____

YY. According to history, where do knee grazing skirts and long slits originate from? _____

_____

ZZ. When slits first invaded the Church, what happened and what were women told to do?
   1. _____
   2. _____

AAA. Detail God's command found in Exodus 20:26.

_____

_____

BBB. Why did God instruct His people not to make steps leading up to His altar? _____

_____

CCC. Is God unconcerned with modesty? _____

DDD. Using your words, tell how God views the uncovering of the woman's legs and thighs according to Isaiah 47:1-4. _____

_____

_____

_____

EEE. Who is God declaring vengeance on in this passage of Scripture? _____

FFF. Name three ways God humiliated the royal princesses.
  1. _____
  2. _____
  3. _____

GGG. Describe how royal women of that day conducted themselves, and name one of the greatest humiliations that could be inflicted on them.
  1. _____

  _____
  2. _____

HHH.　History verifies that _____ was

_____ with _____ while

_____ _____ was a sign of

_____.

III.　In ancient Egypt, what did the slaves and servants wear? _____

JJJ.　Why did aristocrats put on clothes? _____

_____

KKK.　How does God view nakedness?
1. _____
2. _____

LLL.　We are no longer enslaved by sin, but have been made what unto God? _____
1. The Church is spiritual _____, a

_____ _____.

2. Should heaven's royal family expose their flesh in view of common man? ____

MMM. What essential doctrine have we taught through the years (Deuteronomy 22:5)? _____

_____

NNN.   A woman can wear a dress and be _____ or even _____.

OOO.   Write the fashion commentator's quote found on pages 7~~5-76~~. _____
_____
_____

PPP.   What kind of effect does the slit skirt produce?
_____

    1.   When slits are worn open to or above the knee, what are exposed when the wearer walks and climbs stairs? _____

    2.   FOOD FOR THOUGHT: If you cut off your skirt where the slit ends, would you still be able to wear it? _____

QQQ.   It doesn't matter if saints of God are seen in outfits that are low cut, form fitting, or so revealing that nothing is left to the imagination. **True** or **False**

RRR.   What message is communicated by seductive clothing that is left partially unfastened? ____
_____

1. Do you want your clothes to imply this?

   _____

2. Does this sort of attire glorify God or entice the flesh? _____

SSS. What kind of effect will seductive clothing have upon men who are attracted by what they see? _____

TTT. Under the Mosaic Law, how was the act of adultery punished? _____

UUU. According to the teaching of Jesus, what constitutes the sin of adultery in the New Testament (Matthew 5:27-29), and is it fair to pass this off as being totally incumbent upon the men?

1. _____
2. **Yes** or **No**

VVV. In the Old Testament, how was a rape victim treated versus an adulterer (Leviticus 20:10; Deuteronomy 22:22-29)? _____

_____

_____

WWW.   If a woman wears clothing that incites a man to lust and commit adultery in his heart, will she be held accountable in the sight of God?

_____

XXX.   If her pretty legs and attractive body outshine the light of the Holy Ghost, what has she ceased to do and what does the Word of God assert (I Corinthians 1:29)?

1. _____
2. _____

YYY.   Name two things that our brethren should not have to do because of the clothing that is being worn to the House of God.

1. _____
2. _____

ZZZ.   What has the world become, and what must the Church do?

1. _____
2. _____

AAAA.   What should not assail us in the Church?

_____

BBBB.   Was the issue of immodesty unfamiliar to the New Testament Church? _____
  1. What culture surrounded them? _____
  2. What was common for slaves and athletes? _____
  3. What types of garments did people of high rank wear? _____

    _____

CCCC.   Name two things from this culture that Paul alluded to in his writings.
  1. _____
  2. _____
  3. Identify four things Paul was familiar with in the Gentile society.
    a. _____
    b. _____
    c. _____
    d. _____

DDDD.   From this vantage point, what issue did Paul address (I Timothy 2:9-10)? _____

EEEE.   The word "modest" in the Greek is _____, meaning _____.

FFFF.   Give the definition of "decorous." _____

_____

GGGG.   What instruction is Paul giving to women?

_____

_____

HHHH.   Indecent clothing is acceptable in the wardrobe of a godly woman. **True** or **False**

IIII.   Another key word in this Scripture is translated _____ . The Greek word is _____ , and it means _____

_____

_____.

1. Name three things that characterize the actions of a godly woman.

   a. _____

   b. _____

   c. _____

2. Identify two things that govern a consecrated woman's conduct and clothing choices.

   a. _____

   b. _____

3. How is her reverence for her high calling as a holy woman displayed? _____

_____

JJJJ. One more word that describes the attire of a holy woman is _____. The Greek word is _____, meaning _____

_____

_____.

1. In the fear of God, what should women seriously evaluate? _____

2. What are two languages that can be spoken by our clothing?

a. _____

b. _____

3. Name two things that will enable a saint of God to choose garments that speak of godliness rather than worldliness.

a. _____

b. _____

KKKK. Paul used the word "adorn" in this particular Scripture. Give its definition. _____

1. How did God create women? _____

_____

2. Where is the secret to true and lasting beauty found? _____

_____

_____

LLLL.   Memorize I Corinthians 6:19-20.

MMMM. To what did the apostle Paul liken the body of a believer, and what is the definition of this word?

1. _____
2. _____

_____

NNNN. What is the Greek word that Paul used, and to what does it refer?

1. _____
2. _____

OOOO. What have our bodies become?

1. _____
2. _____

PPPP.   How did the High Priest approach the Holy of Holies? _____

1. What did he give careful attention to? __
   _____

2. Describe his garments. _____
   _____

3. This was a matter of _____ or _____.

4. Why was unholy attire never permissible
   in the holy place? _____
   _____

QQQQ. What should our clothing always exemplify?
   _____

RRRR. Revelation 3:18 admonishes us to buy what
   kind of clothing and why?
   1. _____
   2. _____
      _____

SSSS. We cannot _____ the _____ fabric of
   the _____ with the _____ linen of
   _____. Why not (I Corinthians
   3:16-17)? _____
   _____
   _____

TTTT.   As temples of glory, what are we dedicated to? _____

1. What can desensitize us? _____

    _____

2. How must we keep our garments? _____

    _____

3. Are non-believers free to dress according to their desires? **Yes** or **No**

4. Who determines the manner in which we dress? _____

5. Why?

    a.   _____

    b.   _____

UUUU.   *"For ye are _____ with a _____ : therefore _____ God in your _____ !!"*

VII.
Glorify God in Your Spirit

A. Holiness is much more than a list of guidelines that govern a person's outward appearance. How is perfected holiness depicted (II Corinthians 7:1)? _____

B. Identify the weightier matters of the law.

    1. _____

    2. _____

    3. _____

        a. If these components are absent, how is one's perspective of holiness affected? _____

                _____

        b. What does this result in? _____

                _____

C. How does contention come into our lives? ____

_____

D. What kind of attitudes are cultivated by conceit?
   1. _____
   2. _____

E. In your own words, describe satan's most insidious ploys. _____

_____

   1. What will flourish in the fertile soil of pride? _____
   2. When these spirits gain control, does true holiness still exist in your life? _____

F. If there is no love in a church, what has that church become like? _____

G. List seven inward things that are of the world and are not holy.
   1. _____
   2. _____
   3. _____
   4. _____
   5. _____

6. _____

7. _____

H. Describe the type of people whom Jesus was referring to in the parable of the publican and the Pharisee (Luke 18:9-14). _____

_____

1. Who went down to his house justified?

_____

2. How can we tell if our motives or intents are wrong? _____

_____

I. When you speak evil of your brother and judge him, what are you really doing (James 4:11)?

_____

_____

1. What does this cause you to become?

_____

2. Can you engage in this kind of evil speaking and also be obedient to God's Word?

_____

3. Who is the only one qualified to sit in the judgment seat (James 4:12)? _____

J.   Why did Jesus rebuke the Pharisees and label them as hypocrites (Matthew 23:25-26)? _____

_____

    1.   What constitutes a Pharisee? _____

           _____

    2.   Is it possible to look good on the outside and be filthy inside? _____

    3.   When you have true holiness on the inside, how will it manifest itself? _____

           _____

K.   Who was the first one to be perfect in outward beauty, and what was he filled with?

    1.   _____

    2.   _____

L.   In Matthew 23:27-28, how did Jesus depict the Pharisees? _____

_____

M.   What is a hypocrite? _____

_____

N.   A _____ exterior can actually _____ a _____ of _____ filled with the

_____ of innocent _____ who have

been _____ by _____ _____.

O. Paul emphasizes the proper attitudes for the inner man in Colossians 3:12-15. Name five things he said to put on.

1. _____
2. _____
3. _____
4. _____
5. _____

    a. If any man has a quarrel, how should we respond? _____

    b. What is the bond of perfection?

    _____

    c. What should we let rule in our hearts? _____

    d. Why? _____

    e. Finally, Paul told us to *"be ye _____."*

P. How is iniquity purged, and what causes men to depart from evil (Proverbs 16:6)?

1. _____
2. _____

Q.	In what manner should the truth be spoken (Psalm 85:10; Ephesians 4:15-16)?_____

    1.	Whose image will be reflected in our lives when this happens? _____

    2.	How will the body of Christ be affected?

    _____

R.	Define how the Church is supposed to worship the Lord (I Chronicles 16:29; Psalm 29:2, 96:9).

    _____

    1.	How is this injunction perceived many times?_____

    _____

    _____

    2.	What does it literally mean? _____

    _____

    _____

S.	Describe the essence of God's nature (Exodus 15:11; Isaiah 6:3). _____

    _____

T.	What did God command us (I Peter 1:16)? _____

    _____

U.   Holiness standards are much more than a list of dos and don'ts. Explain their purpose. _____

_____

_____

V.   How are we supposed to walk (Ephesians 5:8)?

_____

W.   As we are cleansed inside and out from the bondage of sin, the vestiges of satan's control are eradicated from our lives. What is the end result? _____

_____

X.   Are outward holiness standards by themselves able to save us? _____

   1.   What brings salvation? _____

      _____

   2.   In what manner is this inward work of the Spirit reflected in the life of a true child of God? _____

      _____

   3.   How is God glorified in us? _____

      _____

May the words of this old hymn be our prayer. . . .

Let the beauty of Jesus be seen in me
All His wonderful passion and purity
O Thy Spirit divine all my nature refine
Till the beauty of Jesus be seen in me!

VIII.
Chosen to
Be Special

A. *"For thou art an* _____ _____ *unto the* _____ *thy God: the* _____ *thy God hath* _____ *thee to be a* _____ *people unto* _____*, above all* _____ *that are upon the* _____ *of the* _____ *"* (Deuteronomy 7:6).

B. How does the saga of God's chosen people begin (Genesis 12)? _____

C. Name the first three men who responded to God's call.

1. _____

2. _____

3. _____

        a.   Why was Esau hated (Genesis 25:29-34; Malachi 1:2-3; Romans 9:13)? _____

                _____

        b.   What was inherent in these three men of faith? _____

                _____

D.   Why did God set His love upon Israel (Deuteronomy 7:7-8)? _____

_____

    1.   Who were they favored above? _____

                _____

    2.   What did they receive? _____

E.   Israel comprehended the rare privilege that she had been granted. **True** or **False**

    1.   Who did she choose to serve (Judges 5:8)? _____

    2.   What did a wandering eye of unfaithfulness cause Israel to do?

        a.   _____

        b.   _____

    3.   What was the end result? _____

_____

4. How did God respond to their disobedience? _____

F. Israel's backsliding opened a door of blessing for whom (I Peter 2:9-10)? _____

G. We are the _____ of _____ and have become the _____ of _____ .

H. What is one of the most exciting times in a woman's life, and what is this a picture of?
   1. _____
   2. _____

I. Describe the wedding gown of the Bride of Christ (Revelation 19:8). _____
   _____

J. What kind of Church is God returning for (Ephesians 5:27)? _____

K. As a natural bride delights in her unique bridal attire, what should the Church delight in? _____
   _____

L.   We are _____ of God and made _____.

M.   According to the parable found in Matthew 22, how many times was the Jewish nation bidden to the wedding? _____

    1.   Name two things that were more important to them.

        a.   _____

        b.   _____

    2.   How did they treat God's messengers?

        _____

    3.   What happened to their city? _____

        _____

    4.   How did the King respond to their behavior? _____

        _____

N.   Who has God called to the marriage feast, and where will they be gathered from?

    1.   _____

    2.   _____

O.   After accepting the invitation, what is the responsibility of each guest? _____

_____

1.   What claims are being made by many in the world? _____

    _____

2.   Their deception will lead to what kind of action? _____

    _____

3.   When the King appears at the marriage feast, who will He confront? _____

    _____

4.   What will be the response of these deceived people? _____

    _____

5.   What will happen to them as a result of their disobedience? _____

    _____

P.   *"For many are _____, but _____ are _____ "* (Matthew 22:14).

Here are some questions to ponder:

➢   What choices will the latter day Church make?

➢   Will we accept God's marriage proposal and choose the positive power of holiness, or will we follow the compromising course of world-liness?

➤ Will we reflect Lucifer's likeness or God's glory?

Our choices will determine our destiny!

➤ Which standard of beauty will you emulate?

➤ Will you opt for the world's version portrayed in the similitude of a painted prostitute complete with bobbed hair, Egyptian eyes, fake fingernails, painted toenails, jewelry, and seductive clothing?

➤ Or will you choose God's beauty ideal embodied in the form of a pure, chaste, virgin bride arrayed in fine linen, who reflects His glory on her head and face and in her body and spirit?

➤ How long will God live with His wife?

➤ Can He afford to be choosy?

➢   Why will His Bride be chosen?

➢   Are you chosen to be special?

"For he is Lord of lords, and King of kings: and they that are with him are <u>called, and chosen, and faithful</u>" (Revelation 17:14).

NOTES

NOTES

NOTES

NOTES

NOTES